BOOK 3

Mark Sarnecki

Elementary Music Theory

2nd Edition

FREDERICK
HARRIS
MUSIC

19 18 17 16 15 14 13 12   3 4 5 6 7 8 9 10

Preface

There is no better time to begin theory lessons than in the first formative years when a student begins to study an instrument. This book is designed to complement any piano method. It contains exercises in recognition of the keyboard, music notation, time values, and musical terms. *Elementary Music Theory* is a series of books designed to teach basic music theory and reinforce information learned in the practical lesson.

Mark Sarnecki

Contents

The Harp

The harp is one of the oldest known instruments. It consists of a frame to which a number of strings are attached. The strings are plucked or strummed with the fingers and thumbs.

The oldest harp we know of comes from Asia and is nearly five thousand years old. In earlier times, small harps were used to accompany voices or other instruments. Small harps are also heard in the folk music of a number of countries.

The modern harp was designed by Sébastien Érard in 1810. It is six feet high and has forty-seven strings. The frame is made of wood and the strings are wire, gut, or nylon. The harp also has seven pedals that are used to raise or lower the pitches of the strings. Composers have used the delicate sound of the modern harp in chamber music and in orchestras. There are also harp concertos and solo pieces for harp.

Ledger Lines

We use small lines called **ledger lines** to extend the range of the staff. These lines are used for notes that are above or below the treble and bass staves. Middle C is on a ledger line.

Here are some notes on ledger lines above and below the treble staff.

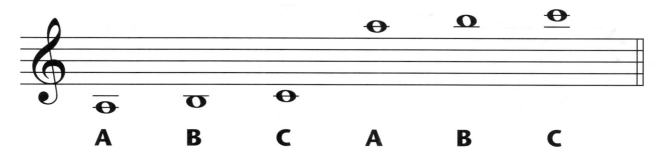

Here are some notes on ledger lines above and below the bass staff.

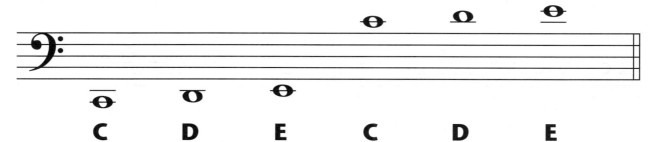

When drawing ledger line notes, always space the ledger lines the same distance apart as the lines of the staff.

Ledger Lines

1. Name the following notes.

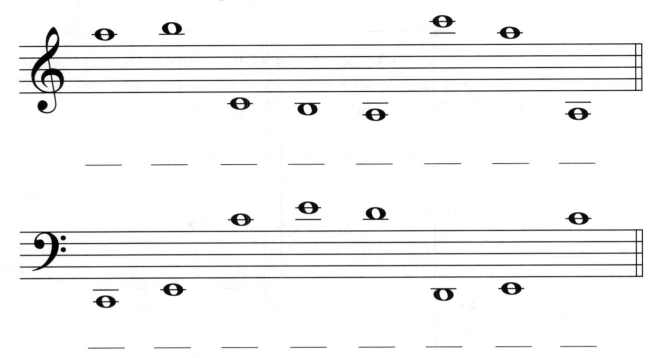

2. Write the following notes using ledger lines above and below the staves. Make sure no two notes are the same.

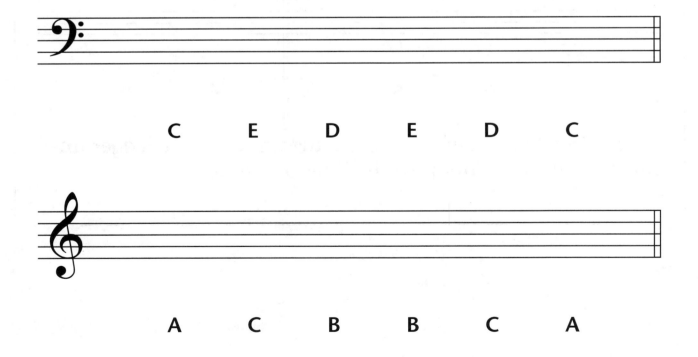

3. Name the following notes.

The Harpsichord

The harpsichord is a keyboard instrument that has the same general shape as a modern grand piano. The main difference between the harpsichord and the piano is that the strings on a harpsichord are plucked. (On a piano, the strings are struck with small hammers.)

Unlike the piano, the harpsichord cannot produce a large range of dynamics or long sustained tones. The keyboard is also shorter. Harpsichords come in a variety of sizes. Many have two sets of strings and two keyboards.

From the late 16th century to the end of the 18th century, the harpsichord was the chief instrument for accompaniment, like the piano is today. Composers such as Bach, Handel, and Purcell wrote many pieces for solo harpsichord as well. Today, we often play these pieces on the piano. Do you know any pieces that were written for harpsichord?

Key Signature Review

Review the following key signatures.

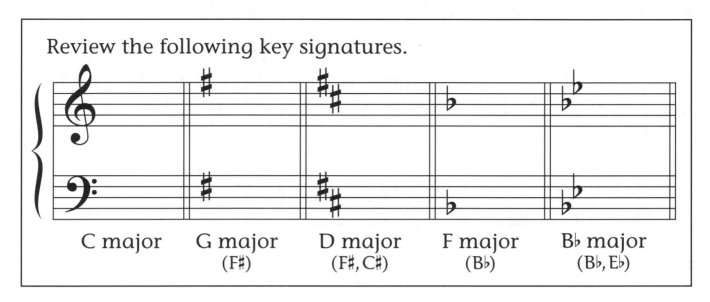

C major	G major	D major	F major	B♭ major
	(F♯)	(F♯, C♯)	(B♭)	(B♭, E♭)

1. Write the following scales using key signatures. Check your key signatures. Make sure the flats or sharps are in the right order and are on the correct lines and spaces.

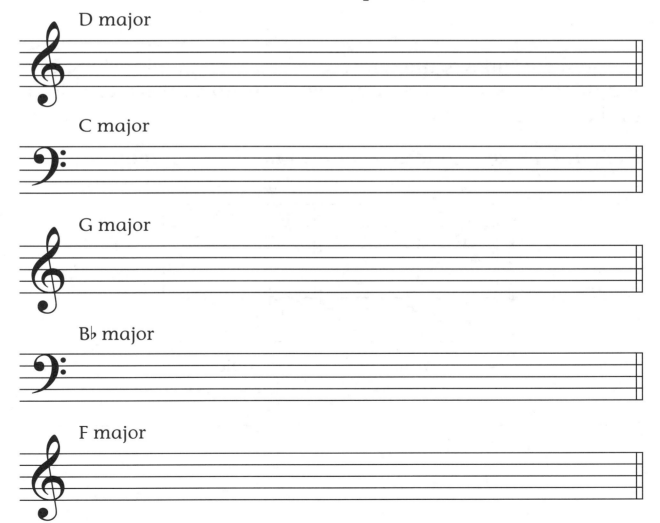

The Scales of A major and E major

The scale of **A major** has three sharps (F sharp, C sharp, G sharp) in its key signature. The scale of **E major** has four sharps (F sharp, C sharp, G sharp, D sharp) in its key signature.

In the scales above, the semitones are marked with slurs. In a major scale, semitones occur between notes three and four, and notes seven and eight.

Here are the key signatures of A major and E major.

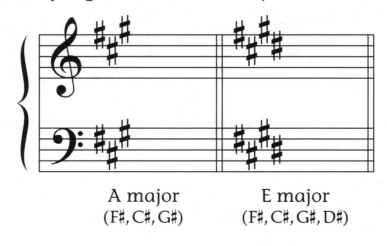

A major
(F#, C#, G#)

E major
(F#, C#, G#, D#)

1. Write the following scales using key signatures. Mark the semitones with slurs.

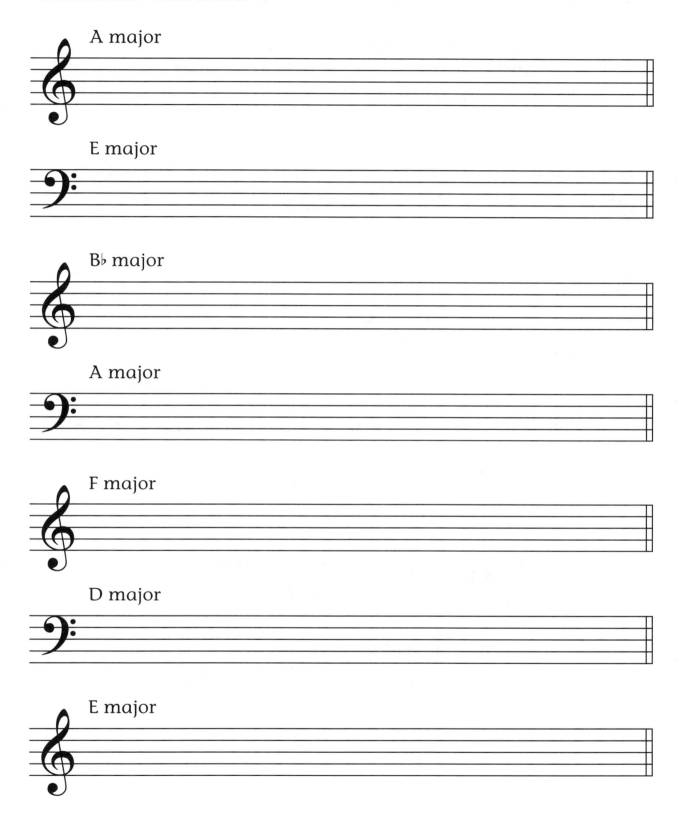

A major

E major

B♭ major

A major

F major

D major

E major

The Scales of E flat major and A flat major

The scale of **E flat major** has three flats (B flat, E flat, A flat) in its key signature. The scale of **A flat major** has four flats (B flat, E flat, A flat, D flat) in its key signature.

Eb major

Ab major

Here are the key signatures of E flat major and A flat major.

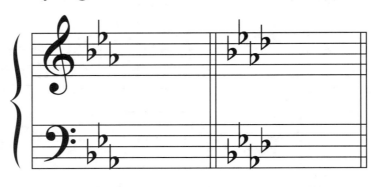

Eb major
(Bb, Eb, Ab)

Ab major
(Bb, Eb, Ab, Db)

1. Write the following scales using key signatures. Mark the semitones with slurs.

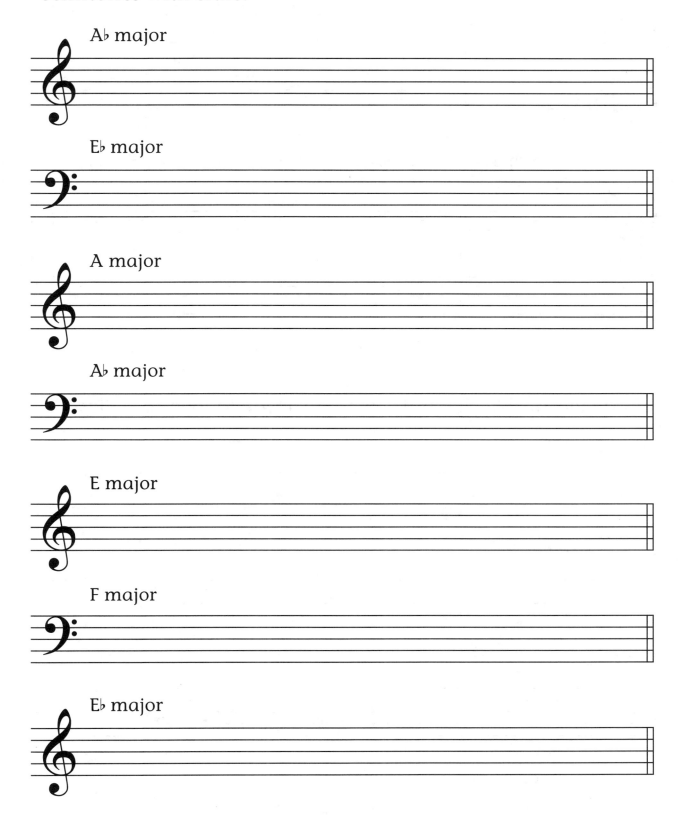

Ab major

Eb major

A major

Ab major

E major

F major

Eb major

Key Signature Review

2. Write the following key signatures on the grand staves below.

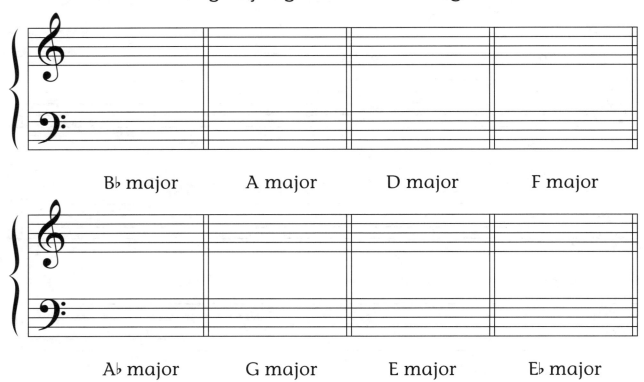

B♭ major   A major   D major   F major

A♭ major   G major   E major   E♭ major

3. Add clefs and key signatures to form the following scales.

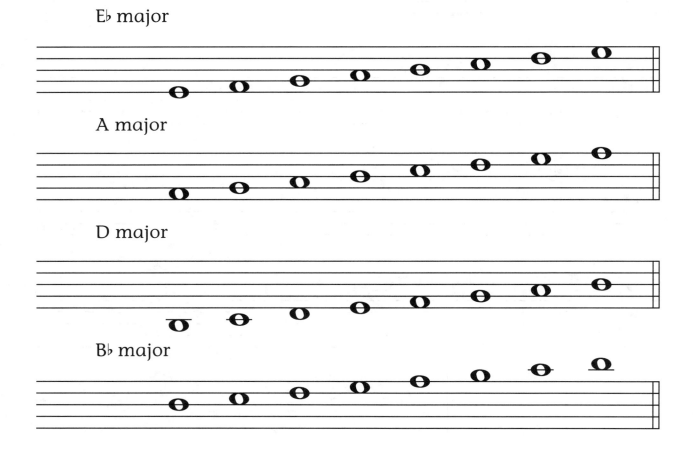

E♭ major

A major

D major

B♭ major

Scales Ascending and Descending

When we play scales on our instruments, we usually play them going up and down. Until now we have only written scales going up (ascending). We can also write them going down (descending).

Look at the following example of G major scale written ascending and descending using a key signature. Remember that when you use a key signature you do not have to write any accidentals in front of the notes. The first note of any scale or key is called the **tonic**. The tonic of C major is C, the tonic of Eb major is Eb, etc. For the following G major scale, the tonic is G and all the Gs have been labeled with a T for tonic.

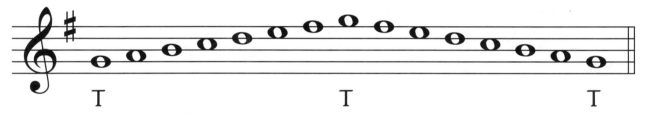

Writing Scales Using Accidentals

When you write scales ascending and descending using accidentals, you place the accidental in front of each note. You do not have to repeat the accidentals when you descend unless there is a bar line at the top. Here are two ways to write the scale of Eb major using accidentals. One is without a bar line at the top and the other uses a bar line. Notice the placement of accidentals in each scale.

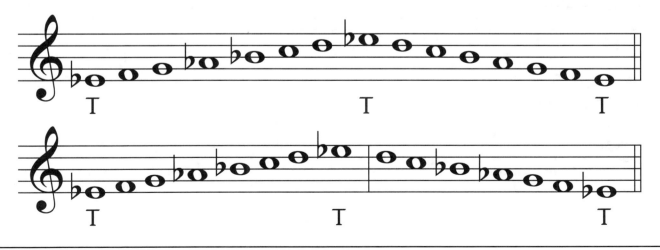

Scales Ascending and Descending

1. Write the following scales ascending and descending using key signatures. Mark the tonic notes on each scale with a T.

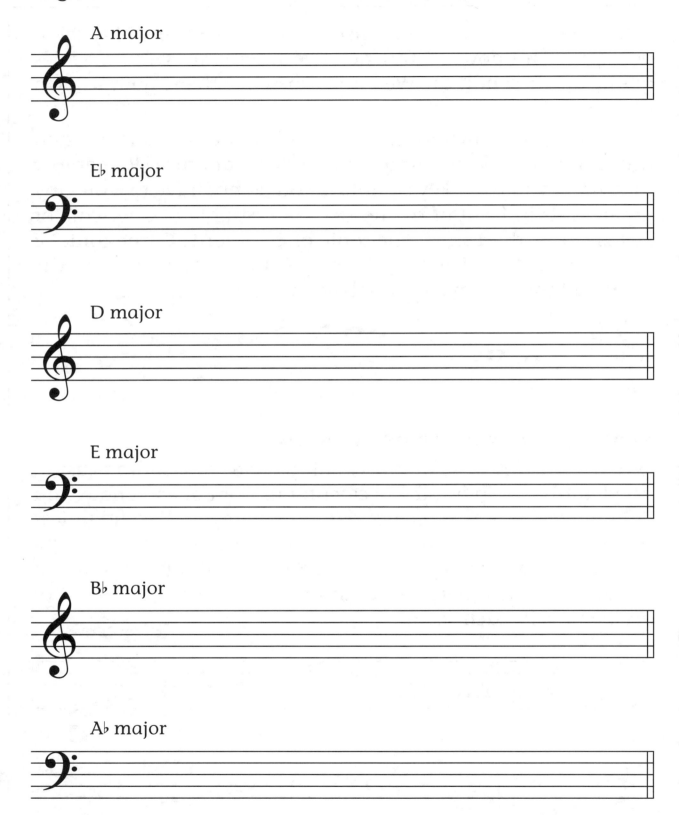

A major

Eb major

D major

E major

Bb major

Ab major

2. Write the following scales ascending and descending using accidentals instead of a key signature. Mark the tonic notes on each scale with a T.

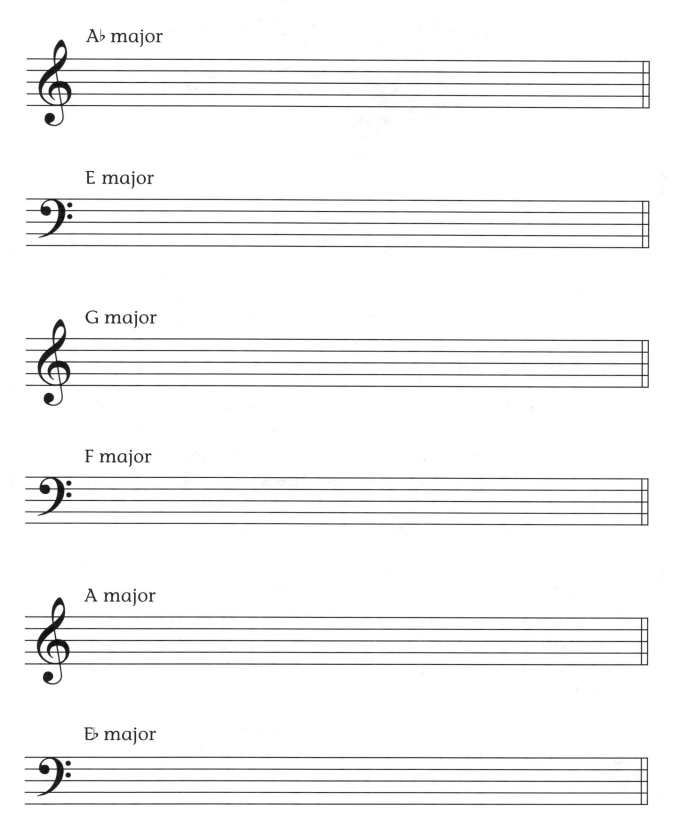

A♭ major

E major

G major

F major

A major

E♭ major

The Piano

The piano was invented around 1700 by an Italian named Bartolomeo Cristofori. He called his new instrument *gravecembalo col piano e forte*—harpsichord with soft and loud. This was an important step forward!

Like the harpsichord, the piano has strings. Unlike the harpsichord, these strings are struck by little hammers. The stronger the touch on the key, the harder the hammer strikes the string, and the louder the sound. Also, unlike the harpsichord, the strings of the piano could resonate for some time. These new possibilities excited composers!

By the end of the 18th century, the piano had replaced the harpsichord on the concert stage. During the 19th century, the desire for even stronger and louder pianos led to changes in design. The keyboard was extended from five and a half octaves to seven octaves. Wooden frames were replaced by metal.

Today, pianos are made all over the world in many shapes and sizes—from a nine-foot grand to the little spinet. Who is the maker of your piano?

Semitones and Accidentals

A **semitone** is the shortest distance between two notes.

An **accidental** is a sign placed in front of a note that changes the pitch of the note by raising it or lowering it.

A **sharp** (♯) raises a note by one semitone.

A **flat** (♭) lowers a note by one semitone.

A **natural** (♮) cancels a sharp or a flat.

With the use of accidentals, it is possible for a single pitch to have two different names. For example, F sharp and G flat are two different names for the same pitch, or the same key on the piano.

The same is true for A sharp and B flat. Play an A sharp and a B flat on your instrument. Do they sound the same?

When we change the name of a note without changing its pitch, this change is called an **enharmonic** change.

1. Give another name for the following notes.

G♯_____   E♭_____

B♭ _____   F♭_____

D♯_____   B♯ _____

A♭ _____   F♯_____

C♯ _____   D♭ _____

Chromatic Semitones

A semitone that consists of two notes with the same letter name is called a **chromatic semitone.**

Here are four examples of chromatic semitones.

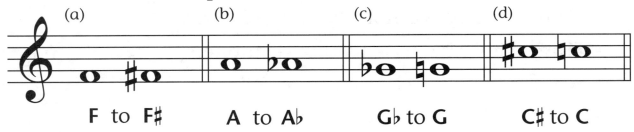

(a) F to F♯   (b) A to A♭   (c) G♭ to G   (d) C♯ to C

(a) A sharp raises a natural one semitone.
(b) A flat lowers a natural one semitone.
(c) A natural raises a flat one semitone.
(d) A natural lowers a sharp one semitone.

1. Write chromatic semitones above the following notes.

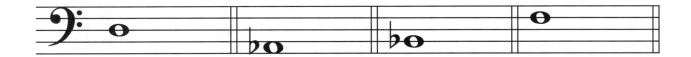

2. Write chromatic semitones below the following notes.

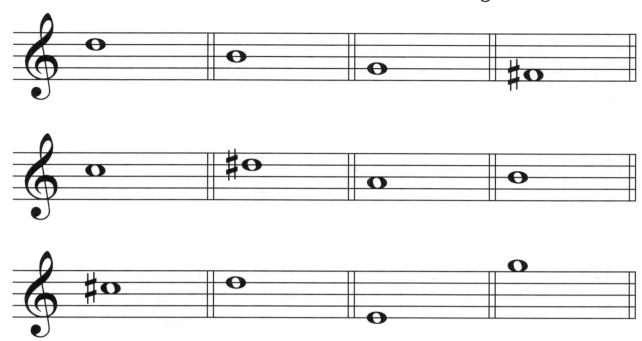

Diatonic Semitones

A semitone that consists of two notes with different letter names is called a **diatonic semitone.**

Here are four examples of diatonic semitones.

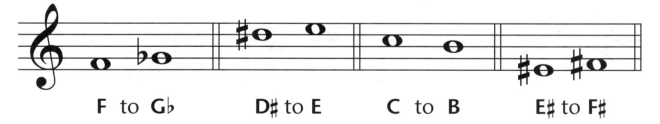

F to G♭   D♯ to E   C to B   E♯ to F♯

Remember that a **whole tone** is made up of two semitones.

On the keyboard, a whole tone is the distance between two keys with one key between them. Whole tones usually have two different letter names. For example, C to D, F sharp to G sharp, and A flat to B flat are all whole tones.

Semitones and Accidentals

1. Write diatonic semitones above the following notes.

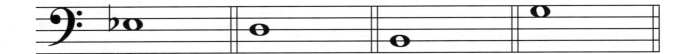

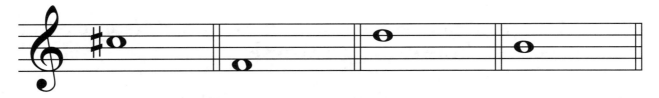

2. Write diatonic semitones below the following notes.

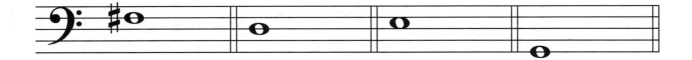

3. Mark the following intervals as chromatic semitones (CS), diatonic semitones (DS), or whole tones (WT).

_____   _____   _____   _____

_____   _____   _____   _____

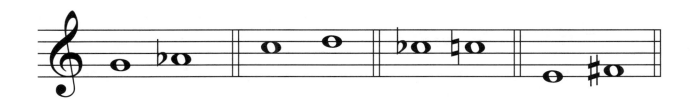

_____   _____   _____   _____

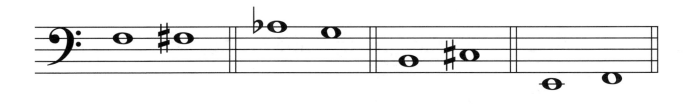

_____   _____   _____   _____

Italian Terms

a tempo	return to the original tempo
cantabile	in a singing style
dolce	sweet, gentle
legato	smooth
M.D., mano destra	right hand
M.S., mano sinistra	left hand

Review Quiz 1

1. Name these notes.

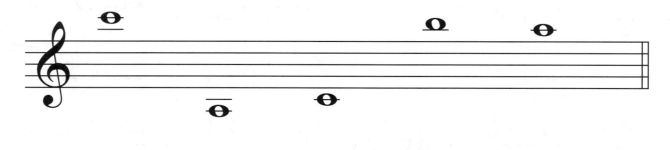

2. Name the sharps or flats in the following keys.

G major _____

E major_____

B♭ major_____

D major _____

F major_____

A major _____

E♭ major_____

A♭ major _____

3. Write the following scales ascending and descending using key signatures for each. Mark the tonic notes with a T.

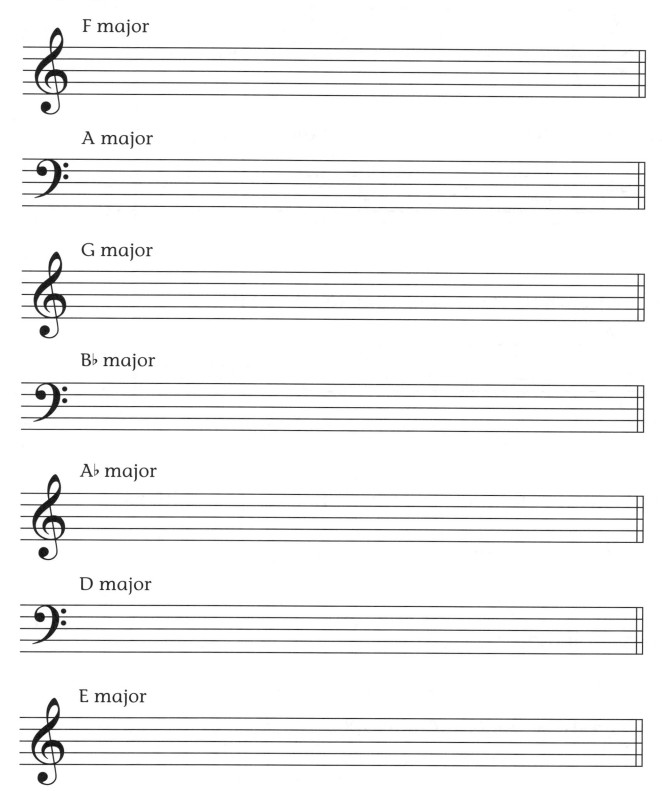

Review Quiz 1

4. Write chromatic semitones above the following notes.

10

5. Write diatonic semitones below the following notes.

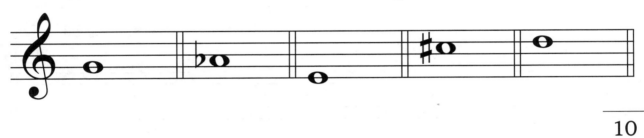

10

6. Write whole tones above the following notes.

10

7. Write the Italian terms for the following definitions.

in a singing style_____

sweet, gentle _____

left hand_____

smooth_____

return to the original tempo _____

9

26   *Elementary Music Theory • Book 3*

The Violin

The violin is made of wood and has four strings. Sound is produced by drawing a bow across the strings. The strings may also be plucked with the fingers—this is called *pizzicato*.

The violin was developed in Italy in the 16th century when Andrea Amati established his violin workshop in Cremona. Over the next century, Amati and his descendants refined the design of the violin. Antonio Stradivarius, an apprentice of Andrea's grandson Niccolo, perfected the instrument. Stradivarius violins are among the most valuable instruments in the world today.

The violin is one of the most important instruments of the orchestra. Violins can play soaring, lyrical lines and dramatic double stops. The violin is also a powerful instrument in solo and chamber music.

Major and Perfect Intervals

An **interval** is the distance between two notes. There are several different types of intervals.

Here are the intervals that are formed between the bottom note and all the other notes of a major scale.

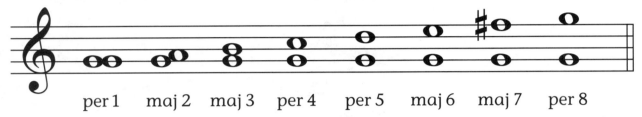

per 1   maj 2   maj 3   per 4   per 5   maj 6   maj 7   per 8

The intervals of a unison, 4th, 5th, and octave are classified as **perfect intervals.**

The intervals of a 2nd, 3rd, 6th, and 7th are classified as **major intervals.**

Think of the bottom note of an interval as the tonic of a major scale.

If the upper note of the interval is a member of the scale of the lower note, the interval will be either perfect or major.

G to **C** is a perfect 4th because **C** is the fourth note of the G major scale.

G to **F sharp** is a major 7th because **F sharp** is the seventh note of the G major scale.

Major and Perfect Intervals

1. Write the scale of D major using accidentals.

2. Write the following intervals above the note D.

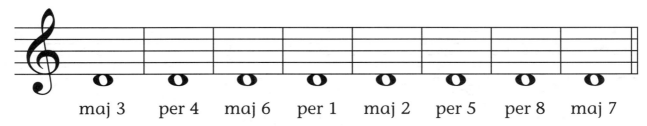

maj 3 per 4 maj 6 per 1 maj 2 per 5 per 8 maj 7

3. Write the scale of F major using accidentals.

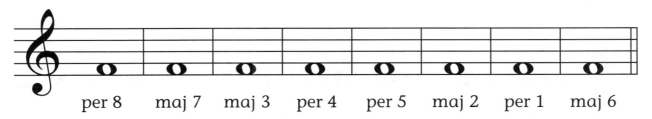

4. Write the following intervals above the note F.

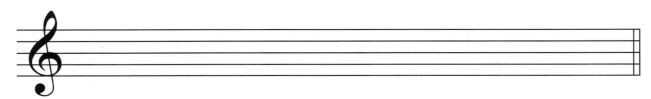

per 8 maj 7 maj 3 per 4 per 5 maj 2 per 1 maj 6

Major and Perfect Intervals

5. Write the scale of E major using accidentals.

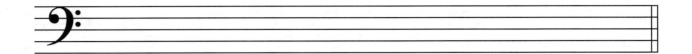

6. Write the following intervals above the note E.

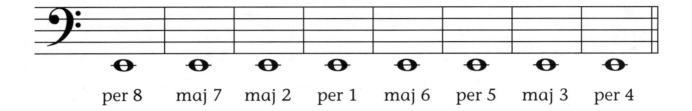

7. Write the scale of A♭ major using accidentals.

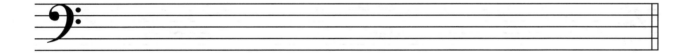

8. Write the following intervals above the note A flat.

9. Name the accidentals in the following keys. Write the intervals above the given notes.

Accidentals in C major _____

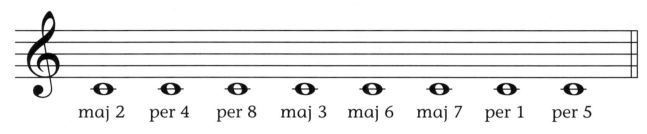

maj 2   per 4   per 8   maj 3   maj 6   maj 7   per 1   per 5

Accidentals in B♭ major _____

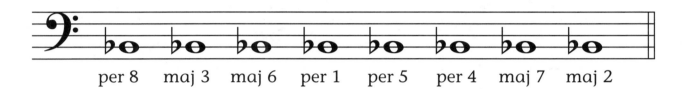

per 8   maj 3   maj 6   per 1   per 5   per 4   maj 7   maj 2

Accidentals in A major _____

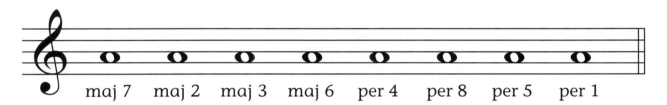

maj 7   maj 2   maj 3   maj 6   per 4   per 8   per 5   per 1

Accidentals in E♭ major _____

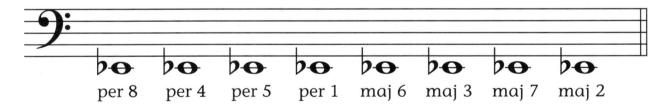

per 8   per 4   per 5   per 1   maj 6   maj 3   maj 7   maj 2

Accidentals in G major _____

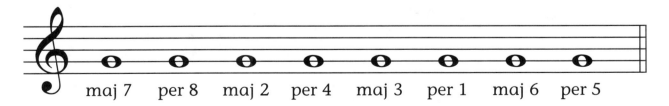

maj 7   per 8   maj 2   per 4   maj 3   per 1   maj 6   per 5

Major and Perfect Intervals

10. Name the following intervals.

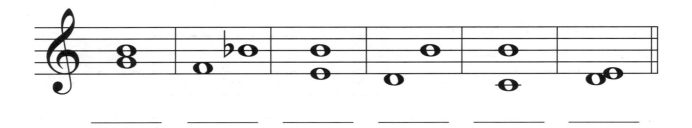

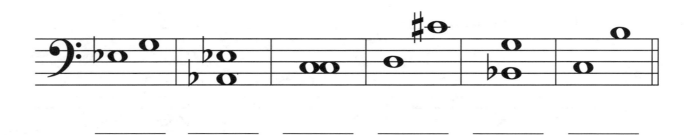

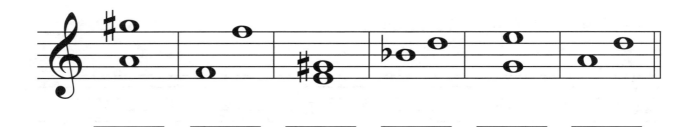

REVIEW

Fill in the blanks using words from the list below.

(a) Small lines called _____ are used to extend the range of the staff.

(b) A _____ is the shortest distance between two notes.

(c) An _____ is a sign placed in front of a note that changes its pitch by raising it or lowering it.

(d) A _____ raises a note by one semitone.

(e) A _____ lowers a note by one semitone.

(f) A _____ cancels a sharp or flat.

(g) A semitone that consists of two notes with the same letter name is called a _____.

(h) A semitone that consists of two notes with different letter names is called a _____.

(i) A _____ is made up of two semitones.

(j) An _____ is the distance between two notes.

interval   semitone
whole tone   sharp
flat   natural
accidental   chromatic semitone
diatonic semitone   ledger lines

MUSICAL WORD SEARCH

Find words from the list below in this puzzle.

M	A	N	O	D	E	S	T	R	A	T	Z	X
A	C	H	R	O	M	A	T	I	C	I	O	P
T	V	M	R	L	P	U	R	C	E	L	L	D
S	A	Q	M	C	A	N	T	A	B	I	L	E
S	C	A	L	E	G	A	P	C	E	D	E	C
E	S	L	D	I	A	T	O	N	I	C	D	O
M	H	V	U	S	L	U	R	O	A	L	G	M
I	A	T	S	H	A	R	P	T	E	E	E	P
T	R	D	C	X	W	A	Q	E	O	F	R	O
O	P	M	P	G	F	L	A	T	R	T	L	S
N	S	R	S	C	A	R	L	A	T	T	I	E
E	D	X	H	A	N	D	E	L	O	E	N	R
H	A	R	P	S	I	C	H	O	R	D	E	S

clef   slur   semitone
chromatic   diatonic   sharp
flat   natural   *cantabile*
dolce   *mano destra*   composers
note   harp   ledger line
scale   harpsichord   Handel
Purcell   Scarlatti

The Clarinet

The clarinet is a single-reed woodwind instrument. Sound is produced by blowing across the reed into the mouthpiece at the top of a cylindrical tube. Clarinets are usually made of African blackwood, but some are made of metal, ebonite, or plastic.

There are several metal keys along the body of the clarinet. These allow the player to produce all the chromatic notes within the clarinet's range. Clarinets have a range of nearly four octaves. Clarinets come in eight different sizes. Each size has a slightly different range. The clarinet in B flat is the most common. Military bands and, of course, jazz groups often use clarinets of various sizes.

The pungent sound of the clarinet is often heard in chamber music groups and symphony orchestras. A number of composers, including Wolfgang Amadeus Mozart, Carl Maria von Weber, and Aaron Copland have written clarinet concertos.

Time Signature Review

2
4 two beats in each measure
   the quarter note gets one beat

3
4 three beats in each measure
   the quarter note gets one beat

4
4 four beats in each measure
   the quarter note gets one beat

1. Add time signatures to the following rhythms.

Dotted Quarter Notes

A dot adds one half the value to the original note.

In $\frac{2}{4}$, $\frac{3}{4}$, and $\frac{4}{4}$, the quarter note receives one beat.

This means that a dot after a quarter note will add half a beat to a quarter note.

♩ = one beat = ♫

• = ½ beat = ♪

♩. = 1½ beats = ♬

A dotted quarter note is equal to a quarter note tied to an eighth note.

♩. = ♩ ♪

1½   1 + ½

Here is one way to count a dotted quarter note.

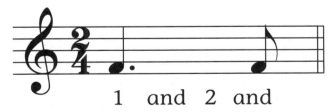

1   and   2   and

Dotted Quarter Notes

1. Add bar lines to these rhythms according to the time signatures.

Sixteenth Notes

A **sixteenth note** looks like an eighth note with an extra flag on its stem.

Two or more sixteenth notes are joined together by two beams.

Two sixteenth notes equal one eighth note.

Four sixteenth notes equal one quarter note.

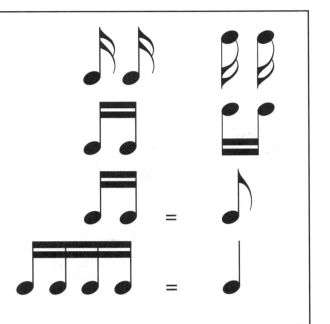

1. Add bar lines to these rhythms according to the time signatures.

Sixteenth Notes

2. Add time signatures to these rhythms.

Triplets

A **triplet** is a group of three notes played in the time of one note of the next larger value.

Not all groups of three notes are triplets. A triplet always has the number *3* over or under the notes.

An eighth-note triplet fills the time of one quarter note.

1. Add bar lines to these rhythms according to the time signatures.

Rests

Music is made up of a combination of notes and rests. Rests indicate durations of silence. There is a saying that, *"notes are silver, rests are golden."* Rests play a very important role in making music.

Review the following rests and their values in quarter time.

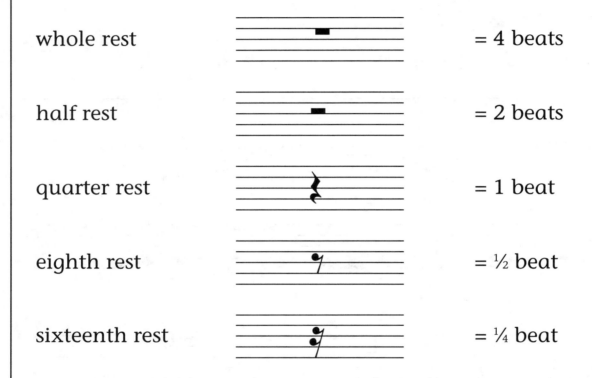

whole rest	= 4 beats
half rest	= 2 beats
quarter rest	= 1 beat
eighth rest	= ½ beat
sixteenth rest	= ¼ beat

A whole rest is used to indicate one complete measure of silence, no matter what time signature is used.

1. Write one rest which is equal to the value of these groups of rests.

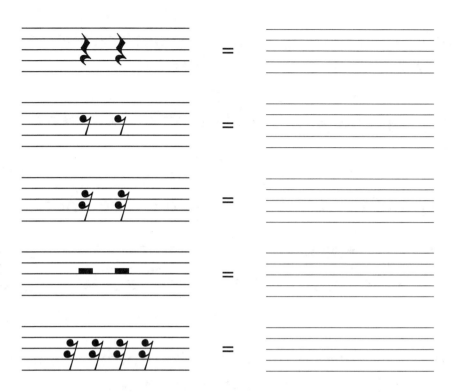

2. Add one rest to complete each measure.

Compound Time

In time signatures with **4** as the bottom number, the quarter note gets the beat. Here is a new time signature:

      6   there are six beats in the measure
      8   the eighth note receives one beat

In $\frac{6}{8}$ time, the measure is subdivided into two groups of three.

The main unit of rhythm is the dotted quarter note.

1 2 3 4 5 6   1 2 3 4 5 6   1 2 3 4 5 6

Time signatures that are organized in groups of three (instead of groups of two) are called **compound time signatures.**

There are two accents in the measure.

    The strong accent is on beat 1.
    The medium accent is on beat 4.

       1 2 3 **4** 5 6
       S w w **M** w w

In $\frac{6}{8}$ rhythms, quarter notes or half notes should not extend across the middle of the measure. Compare these examples.

1. Write the beats under the following measures.

2. Add one note to complete each measure.

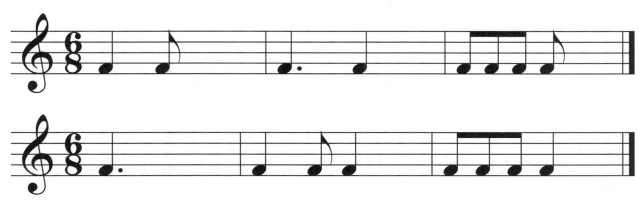

3. Using various rhythms, write three measures of $\frac{6}{8}$ time.

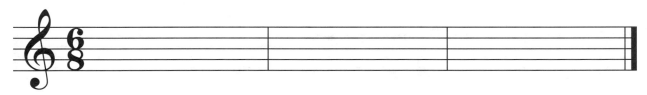

Compound Time

There is an important difference between $\frac{3}{4}$ time and $\frac{6}{8}$ time.

Both time signatures have six eighth notes in a measure, but the accent patterns are not the same.

In $\frac{3}{4}$ time, there are **three** accents in each measure. The six eighth notes fall into groups of **two.**

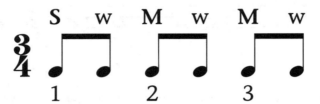

In $\frac{6}{8}$ time, there are **two** accents in each measure. The six eighth notes fall into groups of **three.**

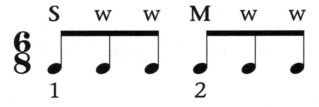

1. Add time signatures to the following rhythms.

2. Add one note to complete each measure.

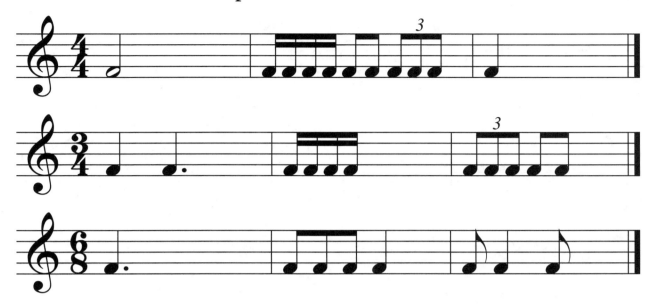

Italian terms referring to tempo

Slow	*largo*	very slow and broad
	larghetto	not as slow as *largo*
	lento	slow
	adagio	slow (slower than *andante,* but not as slow as *largo*)
Medium	*andante*	moderately slow; at a walking pace
	andantino	a little faster than *andante*
	moderato	at a moderate tempo
Fast	*allegretto*	fairly fast (a little slower than *allegro*)
	allegro	fast
	presto	very fast
	prestissimo	as fast as possible

Review Quiz 2

1. Write the following key signatures.

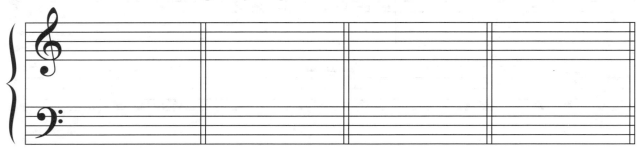

      A♭ major   G major   F major   A major

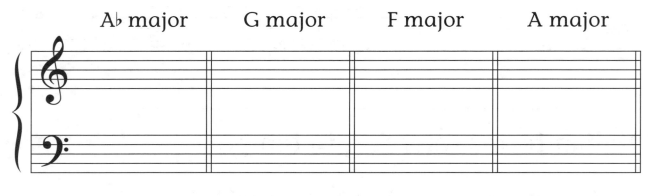

      D major   E♭ major   E major   B♭ major

2. Write the following scales ascending and descending using accidentals instead of a key signature. Mark the tonic notes with a T.

A♭ major

E major

E♭ major

3. Mark the following as chromatic semitones (CS), diatonic semitones (DS), or whole tones (WT).

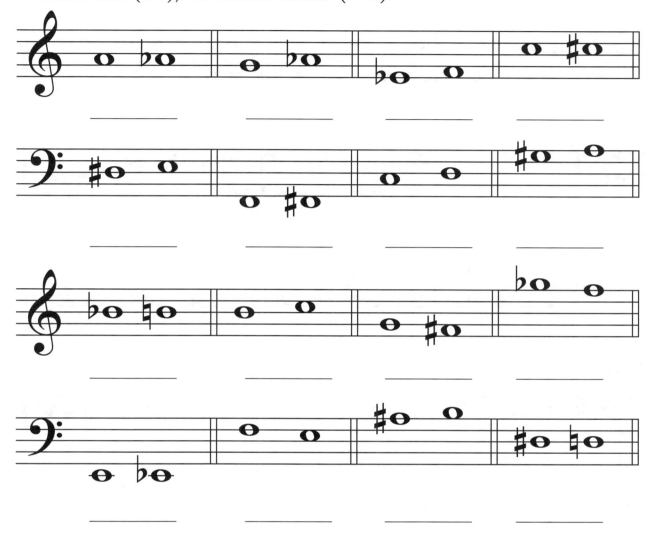

_____ 16

4. Write these intervals above the given notes.

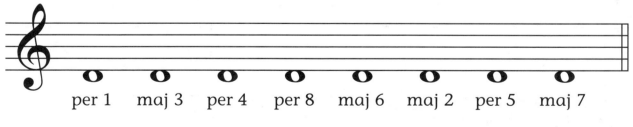

per 1   maj 3   per 4   per 8   maj 6   maj 2   per 5   maj 7

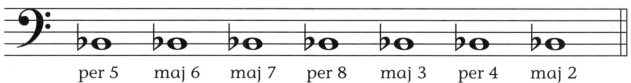

per 5   maj 6   maj 7   per 8   maj 3   per 4   maj 2

_____ 15

Elementary Music Theory • Book 3   49

Review Quiz 2

5. Add bar lines to these rhythms according to the time signatures.

50   *Elementary Music Theory • Book 3*

6. Draw lines matching the following Italian terms with their definitions.

presto	a slow tempo, not as slow as *largo*
adagio	fast
largo	return to the original tempo
allegro	in a singing style
dolce	very fast
mano sinistra, m.s.	right hand
cantabile	as fast as possible
vivace	sweet, gentle
prestissimo	lively, brisk
mano destra, m.d.	very slow
a tempo	left hand

_____
10

The Trumpet

The trumpet is a brass instrument. It has a cup-shaped mouthpiece and a curved narrow tube that widens into a bell at the end.

Like the clarinet, trumpets are made in several different sizes. The most common are the trumpets in B flat and in C. Also, like the clarinet, trumpets can be found in military bands and jazz groups.

The trumpet has a long history. In ancient times, trumpets were played for ceremonial occasions. In the 16th century, composers began to explore the trumpet's musical possibilities. In the 19th and early 20th centuries, composers such as Wagner and Mahler used its brilliant sound in large orchestral works.

Triads

A **chord** is a group of notes that are played together.

A **triad** is a chord that has three notes.

Let's look at a triad that is built on the first note of the C major scale.

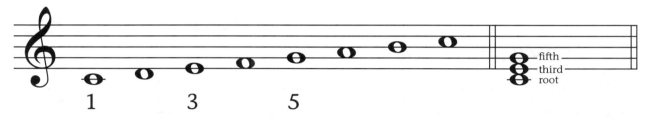

The three notes of a major triad have names:

The bottom note is called the **root.**

The middle note is called the **third.** This note is a major 3rd above the root.

The top note is called the **fifth.** This note is a perfect 5th above the root.

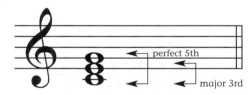

In other words, a major triad is made up of a major 3rd and a perfect 5th.

The first note of a scale is called the **tonic.**

The triad build on the tonic of a major scale is called a **tonic major triad.**

Triads

1. Write the following scales using accidentals. Label the first, third, and fifth notes of the scale (1, 3, 5). Write the tonic major triad for each. Name the triad (C major, D major, etc.).

D major

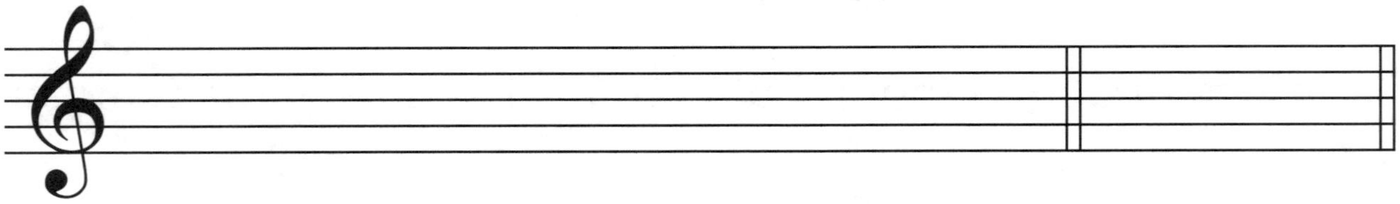

triad name: _____

F major

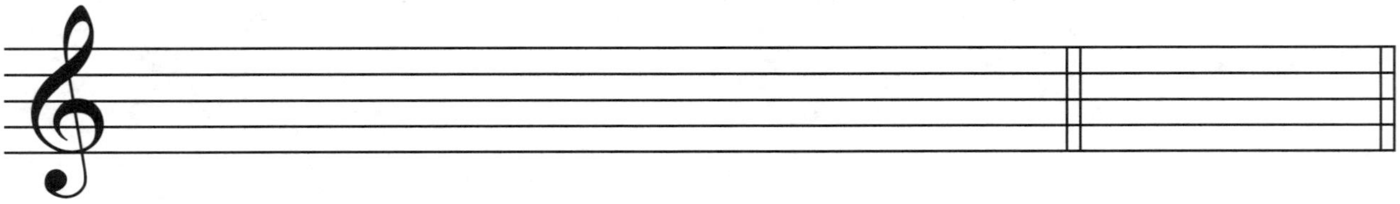

triad name: _____

E♭ major

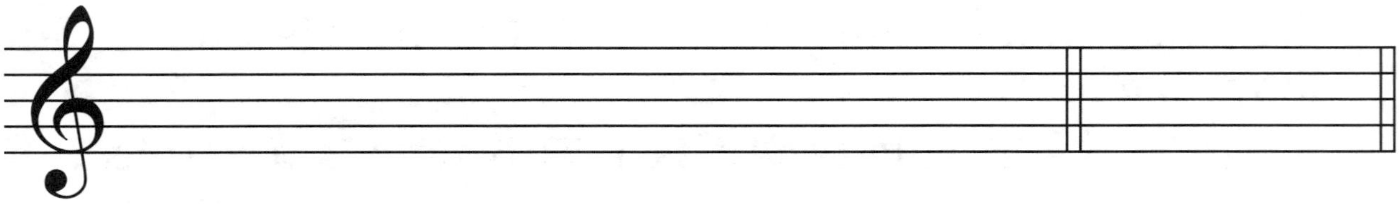

triad name: _____

A major

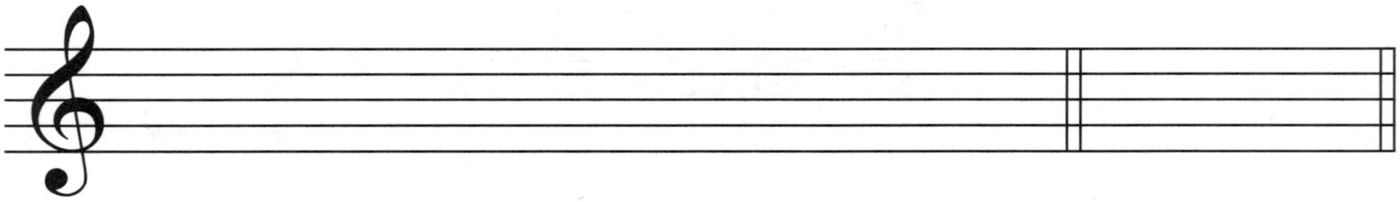

triad name: _____

G major

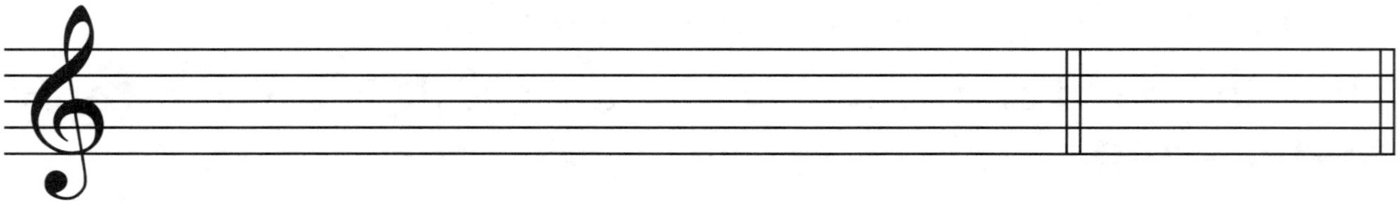

triad name: _____

2. Name the following triads.

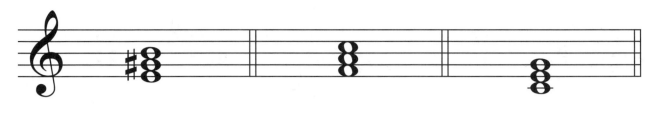

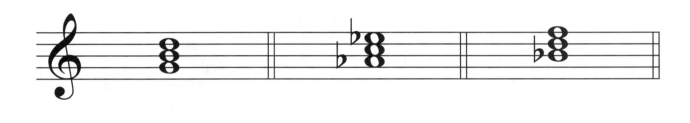

3. Write the following triads.

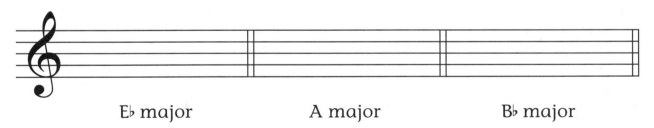

Eb major   A major   Bb major

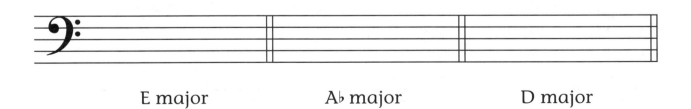

E major   Ab major   D major

Triads

4. Name the following triads.

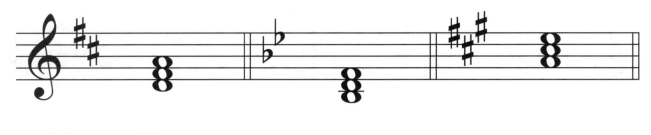

_____ _____ _____

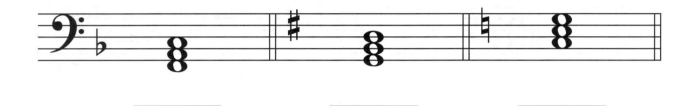

_____ _____ _____

_____ _____ _____

5. Write the following triads using key signatures instead of accidentals.

D major   E♭ major   A major

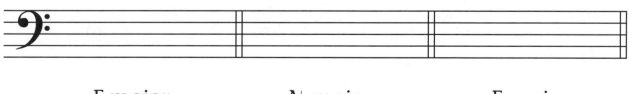

F major   A♭ major   E major

Broken Triads

The notes of a triad may be played **solid** (together) or **broken** (one after the other).

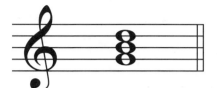 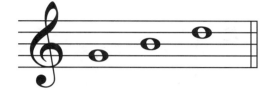

G major triad solid   G major triad broken

1. Write the following broken triads.

B♭ major   G major   D major

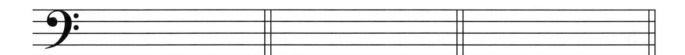

E♭ major   A major   E major

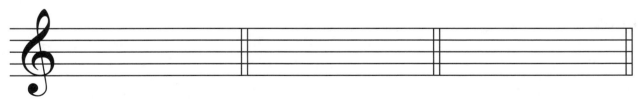

A♭ major   F major   C major

WORD SCRAMBLE

Unscramble these words to find Italian musical terms.

lelrgetota __ __ __ __ __ __ __ (O) __

ntalibcae __ __ __ __ __ __ __ __

garol __ __ __ __ __

leglroa __ __ __ (O) __ __ __

odreatmo (O) __ __ __ __ __ __ __

stismoespri (O) __ __ __ __ __ __ __ __ __

celdo __ __ __ __ __

avceiv __ __ __ __ __ __

tandena __ __ __ __ __ __ __

gadioa __ __ __ __ __ (O)

Copy the circled letters to reveal the hidden word:

__ __ __ __ __

Review Quiz 3

1. Name the following notes.

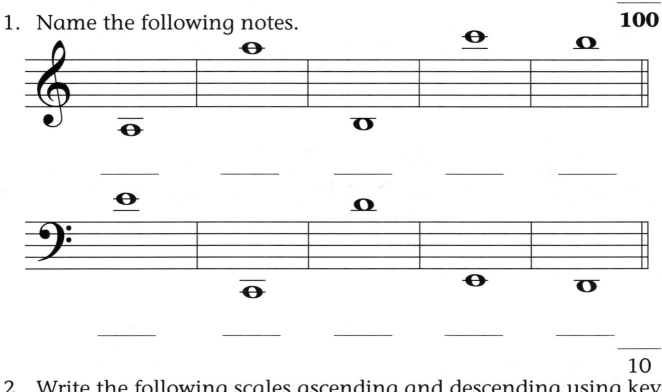

10

2. Write the following scales ascending and descending using key signatures.

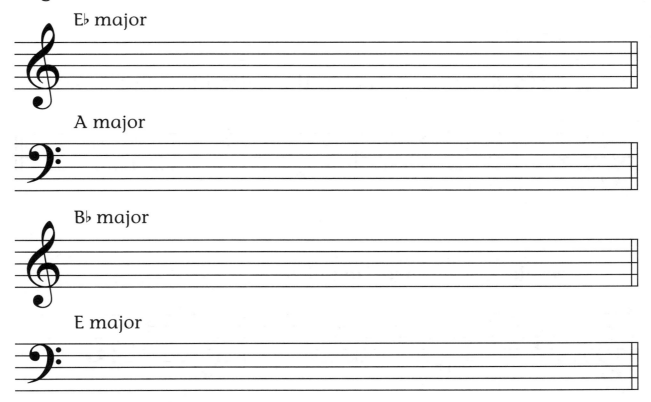

20

Review Quiz 3

3. Name the following intervals.

_____ _____ _____ _____ _____

_____ _____ _____ _____ _____

10

4. Write chromatic semitones above the following notes.

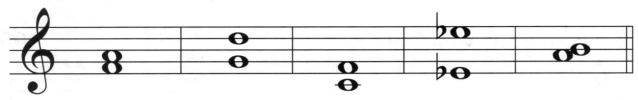

_____
5

5. Write diatonic semitones below the following notes.

_____ 5

6. Write whole tones above the following notes.

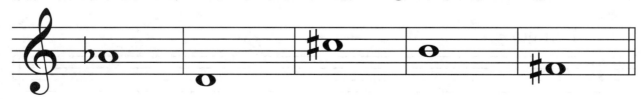

_____
5

7. Add time signatures to the following rhythms.

15

8. Add one rest to complete each measure.

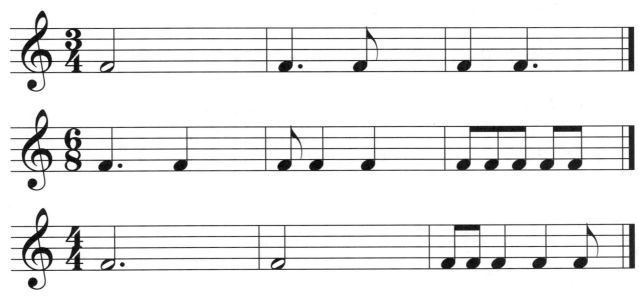

15

Review Quiz 3

9. Write the following triads using accidentals.

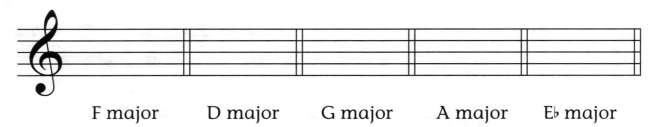

    F major   D major   G major   A major   E♭ major

_____

5

10. Define the following Italian terms.

cantabile _____

presto _____

allegretto _____

mano sinistra _____

largo _____

dolce _____

adagio _____

prestissimo _____

allegro _____

lento _____

_____

10

Music Analysis

1. Analyze the following music by answering the questions below.

Sonatine
Le Bouquetier
op. 151, no. 1

Anton Diabelli
(1781–1858)

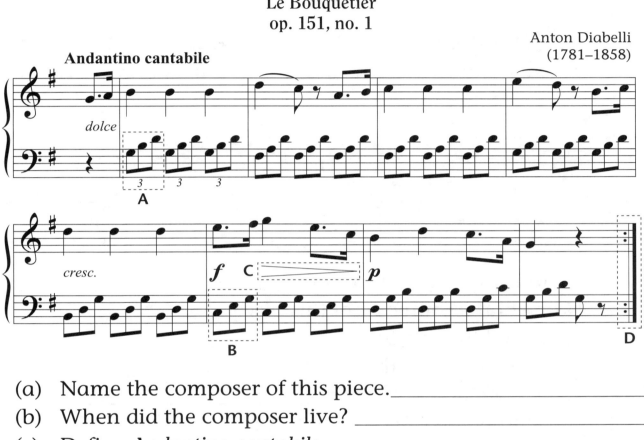

(a) Name the composer of this piece._____

(b) When did the composer live? _____

(c) Define *Andantino cantabile*._____

(d) Define *dolce*. _____

(e) Write the correct time signature on the music.

(f) What is the key of this piece? _____

(g) How many measures are in this piece? _____

(h) Name the broken triad at letter **A**. _____

(i) Name the broken triad at letter **B**._____

(j) Explain the sign at letter **C**._____

(k) Explain the sign at letter **D**. _____

(l) Define *cresc.* _____

(m) What is the highest note in this piece?_____

(n) What is the lowest note in this piece? _____

2. Analyze the following music by answering the questions below.

Menuetto

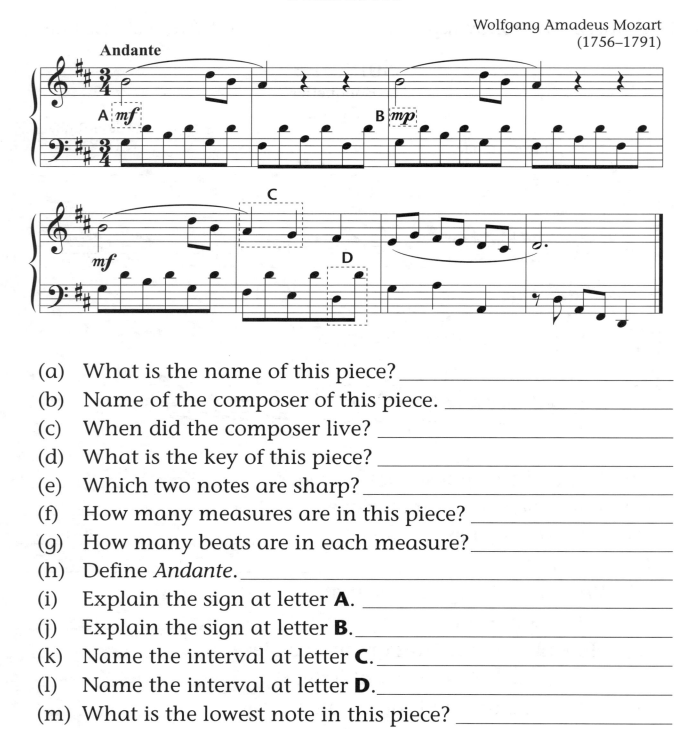

Wolfgang Amadeus Mozart
(1756–1791)

(a) What is the name of this piece? _____

(b) Name of the composer of this piece. _____

(c) When did the composer live? _____

(d) What is the key of this piece? _____

(e) Which two notes are sharp? _____

(f) How many measures are in this piece? _____

(g) How many beats are in each measure? _____

(h) Define *Andante*. _____

(i) Explain the sign at letter **A**. _____

(j) Explain the sign at letter **B**. _____

(k) Name the interval at letter **C**. _____

(l) Name the interval at letter **D**. _____

(m) What is the lowest note in this piece? _____

Congratulations! You have completed
Elementary Music Theory, Book 3.